Young Writers

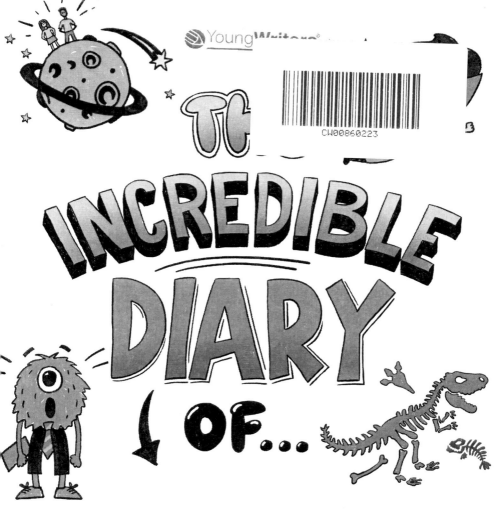

THE INCREDIBLE DIARY OF...

Amazing Tales

Edited By Allie Jones

First published in Great Britain in 2023 by:

Young**Writers**®
— Est. 1991 —

Young Writers
Remus House
Coltsfoot Drive
Peterborough
PE2 9BF
Telephone: 01733 890066
Website: www.youngwriters.co.uk

Printed and bound in the UK by BookPrintingUK
Website: www.bookprintinguk.com
YB0549B

FOREWORD

Dear Diary,

You will never guess what I did today! Shall I tell you? Some primary school pupils wrote some diary entries and I got to read them, and they were EXCELLENT!

Here at Young Writers we created some bright and funky worksheets along with fun and fabulous (and free) resources to help spark ideas and get inspiration flowing. And it clearly worked because WOW!! I can't believe the adventures I've been reading about. Real people, make believe people, dogs and unicorns, even objects like pencils all feature and these diaries all have one thing in common — they are JAM-PACKED with imagination, all squeezed into 100 words!

Here at Young Writers we want to pass our love of the written word onto the next generation and what better way to do that than to celebrate their writing by publishing it in a book! It sets their work free from homework books and notepads and puts it where it deserves to be — **OUT IN THE WORLD!**

Each awesome author in this book should be super proud of themselves, and now they've got proof of their imagination, their ideas and their creativity in black and white, to look back on in years to come!

CONTENTS

Ethan Pearse (11)	56
Finlay Gurnett (11)	57
Martha Cooper (10)	58
Kyle Burton (10)	59
Tulisa Brown (10)	60
Lilly Bentley (10)	61
George O'Sullivan (11)	62
Thomas Pembridge (11)	63
Sam Pearson (10)	64
Rebecca Gledhill (11)	65
Eliora Maturure (10)	66
Riley Sillitoe (10)	67
Ellis Barnes (10)	68
Helena Erzincanoglu (11)	69
Pippa-Rose Baines (10)	70
Kasim Can (11)	71
Cameron (11)	72
Charlie Redhead (10)	73
Veronika Tsymbal (11)	74
Keira Lovatt (11)	75
Logan Darby (11)	76
Ginny Farmer (10)	77
Archie Jackson (10)	78
Corey Timmis (11)	79
Megan Benford (10)	80
Sahara Peach (10)	81
Heidi Stevenson (10)	82
Rosie-Leigh Phillips (11)	83
Declan Bonell (10)	84
Amber Lloyd (10)	85
Sophie Hill (10)	86
Liam Randall (10)	87
Josh McGuinness (11)	88
Hadley Orwell (11) & Bobby Allen (11)	89
Minnie Johnson (10)	90
Poppy Williams (11)	91
Joshua Howson (10)	92
Georgina Bussue (11)	93
Eve Morris (11)	94
Alfie Bailey (11)	95
Edward Pomfret (10)	96
Taylor Hogan (11)	97

Ellis Jones (11)	98
Matilda Chapman (10)	99
Carys Higginson (10)	100
Evelyn Griffiths (10)	101
Oscar Donnelly (11)	102
Emilia Sloan (8)	103
Max Tweddle (11)	104
Isabelle Cadman-Reed (10)	105
Erin Parton (10)	106
Riley Smith (11)	107

New Hall School, Boreham

Peter Ntereba (8)	108
Amelia Craven (8)	109
Bligh Middleton (6)	110

Oxford Education Centre, Cowley

Covenant Ali (10)	111
Mohammed Ibrahimi (10)	112
Tamzin Sibanda (10)	113
Ruwa Musiyarira (7)	114

Park Primary School, Colne

Faye Wellock (11)	115
Kacie Singleton (11)	116
Emily James (11)	117
Shilo Butcher (11)	118
Phoebe Daffern (11)	119

Priorsford Primary School, Peebles

Rowan McNamara (9)	120
Edith Wardman (10)	121
Cian Wilson (10)	122
Harrison Laidlaw (10)	123
Holly Clark (10)	124
Isobel Robertson (10)	125

Rolleston Primary School, Glen Parva

Marley Wye (10)	126
Amelia Jedrzejczyk (9)	127

St Bernadette Catholic Primary School, London Colney

Ethan Wilson (6)	128
Penny Pattison (6)	129

St Margaret's Lee CE Primary School, Lewisham

Daniella Mudizo (10)	130
Elijah (9)	131

St Mary's CE Junior School, Old Basing

Anirudh Pritila (9)	132
Nora Grewal (9)	133
Emma Shahini (8)	134
Isaac Hampton (9)	135
Kiaan Iyer (9)	136
Joshua Porter (9)	137
James Croxon (9)	138
Emmy King (9)	139
Janella Adeliyi (9)	140
Stanley Holmes (8)	141
Lexi Berry (8)	142
Jacob Bolger (9)	143
Ella Head (9)	144
Jax Flood (9)	145
Saanvi Mahika (9)	146
Siri Rikka (9)	147
Elizabeth O'Leary (8)	148
James Condliffe (8)	149
Iniya Sasikumar (9)	150
Alicia Ng (9)	151
Harlie Kipping (8)	152
Thomas Baldwin (9)	153
Eshan Golleru (9)	154
Mia-Lee Kerrigan (9)	155

Isla Sutton (9)	156
Jesse Agyaba Afriyie (9)	157
Spencer Andrews (9)	158
Rose Williams (9)	159
Jack Fox (8)	160
Sophie Rolls (8)	161
Annabelle Huxham (8)	162
Abeer Pandey (8)	163

St Wilfrid's Catholic Primary School, Angmering

Archie Hillier (11)	164
Delta Murphy (10)	165

Westwood Primary School, Lowestoft

Francesca Ellyatt (7)	166
Ciara Pettinger (6)	167
Marnie Baldry (7)	168
Leni Tuttle (7)	169

Youlgrave All Saints CE (VA) Primary School, Youlgrave

Esme Tory (9)	170
Daisy Bingham (10)	171
Darcy Moorhouse (10)	172
Imogen Room (11)	173
Oriel Carlin-Monkhouse (10)	174

I Have A Superpower

Dear Diary,

Today was great. First, I went to school, but it wasn't just an ordinary school day. We were going to Cadbury's Chocolate World! First, we tried all the chocolate there. Then we went to see all the chocolate. Then we went to see a short movie. Then I realised I had superpowers because someone was about to be sick and I looked away and put my hand in front and it froze them. Then I very slowly carried them to the bathroom and unfroze them and quickly closed the door and then I went back home.

Lucy Gobbett (7)
Ashbourne Primary School, Ashbourne

The Diary Of A Pink Bunny

Dear Diary,

Today I got lost in the deep, dark woods. This is how it happened.

I was going to pick some carrots with my mum. Just then, I saw a beautiful butterfly and I chased it into the dark wood. I got lost in the wood. I was so scared. Just then, I heard some wolves and started running. I could still hear them, so I kept running. I saw the light and ran as fast as I could go. I finally got out of the dark wood. My mum saw me and said, "We were looking for you."

Amy Wibberley (8)
Ashbourne Primary School, Ashbourne

Try To Catch A Unicorn

Dear Diary,

I went into the forest and saw a unicorn. I thought I could have it as a pet and I rode the unicorn. I brought it home and it almost filled my whole house up. She did rainbow poos in the house and every day she climbs on the table. I took the unicorn to school and let all my friends ride and stroke it. My unicorn showed me an amazing dance. My unicorn once got lost in the forest. My unicorn is sad and I don't know why. I love unicorns lots.

Ellie Glover (5)
Ashbourne Primary School, Ashbourne

The Football Stadium!

Manchester City vs Manchester United, 2022/23, FA Cup Final. A heated matchup. "It's the sixty-second minute and Bernardo Silva seems to be down injured. Oh, my! He's been shot twice and is injured!" someone shouted. "A Man Utd fan is being chased, he's got a gun!"
So the chase was on. We chased him onto the main road and we cornered him at the junction. His name was Elliot Haydew, thirty-six years of age, a lunatic who had escaped from Manchester Lunatic Asylum. Two weeks later, Sky News said, "Bernardo Silva has survived and Elliot Haydew went to prison forever."

Gwilym Hammond (9)

Durston House School, Ealing

Diary Of A Moron

Sunday,

My parents are always telling me to switch my console off and play in the garden, but the way I see it is that I can play football on my Xbox, but for some reason, they don't like it.

Monday,

My first day back at school from Easter holidays and it's been going pretty terribly so far. Let me explain. First of all, I forgot my bag at home, so my mum brought it in and said, "Sweetie, you forgot your bag." I almost died of embarrassment. So now I'm getting bullied at school and that's what happened today.

Tirath Singh Dooa (9)

Durston House School, Ealing

Diary Of A Moany Millipede, The Hard Find

Dear Diary,

Some big guy stepped on my house today and it got crushed, moan!

Mum said, "Quick, get out!" We tried to look for rocks with holes to be our new home. Some were too wide or damp to be a house. Then, we found a house next to a pristine lake, but it wasn't a good fit because it only had a boring bookshelf. Finally, we found a good house after days of searching. Dad said, "Feel comfy!" It had everything. TVs, games, a sandwich; why was that there? It was the big guy's yummy lunch - not anymore!

Reyaan Gupta (8)

Durston House School, Ealing

Diary Of King Viraj's Life

Dear Diary,

Today I am being coronated. It has always been my dream to live in Buckingham Palace. There is a chocolate fountain, luscious green gardens and flowers made of red strawberries and gooey marshmallows. The green garden has pavements made of colourful Skittles and Smarties. The large bedroom is so spacious I can play hide-and-seek. Today I'm going to be a King. Why am I shaking or feeling scared? Will I be a good or a bad King? I want to be a good and helpful King. I want to serve everyone with love and respect.

Viraj Singh Chandhok (9)

Durston House School, Ealing

A Diary Of Two Days

Dear Diary,
Today there was a big fuss about the cheesecake. People were complaining that they had smaller slices than other people. The dinner portions were too small, so I got a straw to make it last longer. I guess that's what happens when you have three other people in the house. Today, in the morning, we went to school. People were staying in because it was very icy that day. Cars skidding on the road. After school today, my dad took us to the shop and everything got crazy. We all split up and the alarm went off.

Spencer Jaher (8)
Durston House School, Ealing

Train Murder

Finally, I was boarding the Runaway Eagle. I had my own private room that had a mind-blowing view. After I finished unpacking, it occurred to me that I should explore the loco. Whilst I passed the dining carriage, a man was bragging about how fun it was to be a poacher and that he had brought his gun with him on the train. A safari ranger was reprimanding him that he would suffer his wrath if he killed an animal. Later that day, I heard a scream. I rushed towards the room, only to realise that the poacher was murdered.

Shlok Kher (9)
Durston House School, Ealing

The Incredible Power Of Dreams

Dear Diary,

Today I was amazed to find I could fly, but then I realised that this superpower would come with at least a few knocks and bumps. I thought about all the cool stuff I would be able to do, like slaying dragons, fighting trolls, and saving cities. I couldn't wait to get going. I summoned a portal which I didn't know I could do. I went through and found myself surrounded. Then I woke up. Sadly, it was a dream and I need to remember the dream. I hope the day goes quickly so I return to sleep!

Oscar Renshaw (9)

Durston House School, Ealing

Bob's Diary: Today I Am Grounded

Dear Diary,

Today I am grounded. I am canary by the way. So this is how I became grounded. My best friend James told me that the inexorable, evil pigeon Tillick's staff, is very magical, so I went to steal it because my brother Robert said it was a good idea. I got hurt but I was still able to steal it. So that is how I got grounded. My brother Fred had tried to prove that I should not be grounded, which I appreciate, but I am still frustrated that Robert did not become grounded for the idea.

Ryan Salehi (9)
Durston House School, Ealing

Diary Of A Cricket God

For some reason, my dad wanted me to play cricket! Isn't that an insect? He wanted me to play a sport named after an insect!
I went to training. It wasn't that bad. I hardly knew what armour to wear. Cricket pads, box, what is this stuff? The day after that, we played a match. I was completely useless at batting. I scored just one run. I was much better at bowling. When I bowled, the ball flew in the air. A fielder caught it. "Out!" I got my first wicket! I was so excited.

Ayan Varma (8)
Durston House School, Ealing

The Best Holiday Ever!

Dear Diary,

I had the best day ever today! I've never felt so happy. We arrived in Greece two days ago. It is extremely hot here. On our first day, we went to a beautiful sandy beach and I played in the sea for hours. Today was even better! we travelled to a colossal waterpark. My mum and I were playing on the slides, until a pretty girl my age asked me to play with her. Olivia and I spent the whole day on gigantic slides and eating ice cream. We will be best holiday friends forever!

Shye Buckenham (8)
Grove Primary School, Carlton Colville

A Day At Swimming

Dear Diary,

Today I went swimming with my auntie and my sister. We took the bus. I felt happy. When we got off the bus, we walked to the swimming pool. When we got inside, we had to get changed and find a locker. First, we went into the splash area. It had a slide. Then we went into the middle pool. It was deeper and more fun. It was nice and warm. The end pool was cold. I did not like it. We got changed and took the bus back home. It was a fun day with my auntie.

Scarlett-Rose Wright (6)

Grove Primary School, Carlton Colville

Rosie The Unicorn

Dear Diary

Today I was running and sliding on a rainbow but when I ran up it, I fell off, but I got back up and had lots of fun. I bounced on the rainbow. It was lots of fun like always and when I ran down, I saw a pot of gold. I ran off with it and ran into the woods and dug a hole in the ground and put the treasure in the muddy hole and ran back to Ice Cream Land and pretended she didn't know what they were talking about!

Amber Martin (6)

Grove Primary School, Carlton Colville

The Amazing Superman!

Hello Diary,

I am so excited to tell you about my day at football. I saw Superman fly onto the pitch and he scored a goal for me. Everyone cheered for Superman. It was time for him to go to save someone who had fallen into the river. He zoomed off the pitch. Everyone fell over because he was going so fast. We all got wet because it had been raining. It made everyone laugh.

Tommy Rogers (6)

Grove Primary School, Carlton Colville

The Beautiful Pigeon

Dear Diary,

Today, I got up and flew around the park (like I always do). Suddenly, I felt extremely thirsty, so I landed next to the nearest puddle. I was oh-so-very bored. But when I looked at my reflection in the water, I wasn't a boring, old pigeon anymore. I was a dove! Everyone thought I was beautiful (I think). I was so busy looking at all my admirers, I didn't notice another dove right in front of me! "I'm so sorry!" I shouted, "Being a dove is distracting." "You're not a dove. You're just beautiful."

Elsie Deriu (9)

Larkrise Primary School, Great Baddow

A Slave From Egypt

Dear Diary,

Today I was working in extreme heat. I had to collect stone, gold, ivory, and spices. I also had to collect wood. If I didn't collect all of this, I would have been beaten. Some of the other slaves got a beating because they couldn't collect it all. Two years ago, I got taken away from my family. I miss them so much. I was a free man. Now, my freedom is completely gone. I am alive but not living! As an Egyptian slave, I get forced to do things I don't want to. When will it stop?

Eva Devoir (10)
Larkrise Primary School, Great Baddow

Ramadan

Dear Diary,

This month called Ramadan has finally arrived. On Ramadan, many people fast. Also in Ramadan, the Quran was revealed to the prophet Muhammad (SAW) which was brought down by angel Jibreel or in English, it would be Angel Gabriel. Before Fajr prayer, we have a small meal called Suhoor and after the Magrib prayer adhan, we have a meal called Iftar to break our fast. It is a sunnah to break our fast with dates. In Ramadan, we pray an extra prayer called Taraweeh after Isha prayer. Ramadan is also the month when Allah (SWT) accepts our duas.

Mustaqim Ayaan (8)

Larkrise Primary School, Great Baddow

Dragon

Dear Diary,
You wouldn't believe what happened. I woke up in a dark and mysterious place. I think it was a castle. I started to see a shadow forming. I looked at myself and I was a blue dragon with ice-water powers. I didn't know how to control myself until the mysterious shadow spoke. It told me that I will only turn into a dragon when I am mad, sad or worried. The only time I will be normal is when I'm happy and calm. If I'm excited, something really bad will happen. Nobody knows what will happen to me...

Francesca Norman (9)
Larkrise Primary School, Great Baddow

The Curse Of The Simulation

Dear Diary,

Today I woke up in a simulation. Everything was different. I could tell the taste was different from what I could remember. Was I taken to this simulation for a reason? I had to do something to leave, even though the simulation was some kind of beast world! I found a cursed sword. It was a dual sword and as I took it out, I saw a terrifying, dreadful dragon. Destructively, it was breathing fire at me! I was trapped and I was frightened but determined to succeed!

I knew I had to lift the curse... but how?

Daniils Udovenko (10)

Larkrise Primary School, Great Baddow

Forgotten Flower

Dear Diary,

Every day I sit in a scruffy, messy patch, where I get stamped and trampled on by large human shoes. In the middle of my lovely day, dirty hands pick me up and start waving me back and forth till my head goes numb and body limp. They sit down on the grass right in front of my friends and start picking and pulling my colourful petals off and rip me apart like I'm a simple piece of matted, plain paper. I don't matter to anyone. Finally, my day is over. I collapse onto the ground, exhausted. Flower.

Muna Ezike (9)

Larkrise Primary School, Great Baddow

Camp Mix-Up

Dear Diary,

I made another mistake. I accidentally signed up for a football camp instead of maths camp and there's no turning back because my parents are in Morocco and there are no spaces left in the maths camp. So now I'm basically stuck in a sports game I've never played in my life. At least there are maths lessons on Tuesdays and Thursdays, but it's not enough for me because they're only twenty minutes. At least I got a goal today because it's my fourth match. I just hope something good happens.

Omar Aljalabheh (9)

Larkrise Primary School, Great Baddow

I Am A Lion

Dear Diary,
You won't believe this! I woke up and started to do my normal schedule before noticing something was different. It wasn't that my sister had coloured my walls with lipstick (I will get her back for that!). It was my reflection in the mirror! Now, I have had many bad hair days but this was something else! Thick fur covered my head. I blinked, thinking I was still dreaming! I was a lion! I tried to scream but a roar came out! What am I going to do? I am starving and I can hear my little sister...

Tamilini Mahesh (10)
Larkrise Primary School, Great Baddow

Veruca's Adventure

Dear Diary,

Earlier, I was in Mr Wonka's luxurious factory and now I've been thrown into a disgusting, smelly bin. I'll explain how this happened... We were in the biggest room, the Nut Room! It was huge, but the only good thing about it was the squirrels. Oh, how I wanted one so badly. Suddenly, I couldn't help it, so I screamed at the top of my lungs. It gave me a sore throat and still no squirrel. Then, I decided to pick one up and bring it home with me. It pushed me down the garbage chute. Just why!

Ruby Shepherd (8)

Larkrise Primary School, Great Baddow

The Larkrise Football

Dear Diary,

Every day, I start in a dark cold room. Then I am brutally thrown and kicked by a hundred children who laugh and cheer through my agony. Painfully, they train with me and practise their skills, which hurt. I get bruised a lot and often end up in the back of a net. A loud whistle is then blown and I'm abandoned outside, often in the rain. I don't like getting wet. Every now and then people hold me with pure love in their hearts! This is the only part of the day I like!

The Larkrise football.

Jamie Berwer (10)

Larkrise Primary School, Great Baddow

Skellig

Dear Diary,

I made a baby come back to life because of her brother. He told me that his sister was not doing good so I decided to make her live. Silently, I crept into the hospital. I saw his mum with the weak, poorly baby. When I moved closer to the baby her mum looked at me with fear. I told her with my eyes I would make her live. Gently, I lifted the helpless creature. Delicate wings appeared from her back as we danced and flew together. I placed her back down knowing she was healed forever! Skellig.

Keira Frappell (10)

Larkrise Primary School, Great Baddow

I Am A Mutant Turtle

Dear Diary,

Today I woke up and something felt different! There was a heavy lump on my back and my skin was completely green all over like I had been dipped in slime! I only had three fingers! I looked in the mirror and saw the lump was a turtle *shell!* A thin, yellow shell covered my belly too! I ran down the stairs in complete shock! I looked out into the garden and four other turtles (that I recognised!) stood there wearing their famous coloured masks! I was an honorary Mutant Turtle for the day!

Baiden Beyers (10)
Larkrise Primary School, Great Baddow

When I Went To The Moon

Dear Diary,

Something happened today. I went to school and there was a rocket. We went on it, but crashed on the moon. We needed to find the fuel. I said we should split up. They said, "Yes, okay." "Come on."

Day 2, we didn't find the fuel, but we explored.

Day 5 we found a lot, but not enough but we found some moon rock.

Day 7 we found a lot of fuel. It was so close.

Day 10, we found all of it and were heading back to school. Got back to school and it was home time.

Max Carline (8)

Larkrise Primary School, Great Baddow

A Girl Called Delaney

Dear Diary,
Today I got up and looked in the mirror and I looked different... I was a weird creature. I was a leopard! Then it came to me. I had powers! A powerful sensation came to me and I ran but don't worry, I was human again. But I got some weird cramps and a craving for a sweet. I set off to begin my journey to help people. I'm still astonished by all this. It turns out I didn't have powers, just a lovely woman-like day that day. I became a beautiful, independent, lovely young woman.

Delaney Batchford (9)
Larkrise Primary School, Great Baddow

The Holy Month, Ramadan

Dear Diary,

Every year when I go to Earth, people fast till sunset. They put decorations in their gardens to show that I have arrived and they also put decorations in their houses. I love to watch the people when they fast and get close to Allah. Allah is Islam's god. Every year, I come in a different month. This year, I came in March. When I go to Earth, people go to the mosque more than usual. As you know, people pray and read the holy book of Islam at the mosque. I have to go and relax.

Nehir Karakus (9)

Larkrise Primary School, Great Baddow

My First Day In My School

Dear Diary,

Today was my first day in my new school. It was not great, there were two kids who were not particularly nice. They would bully me at lunch and break time even when teachers looked. I really didn't go near them, but somehow, they found me. I went to the teachers. They said they would keep an eye on them but they did not do anything about it. They called me names and made fun of my glasses. I really wanted it to stop, but it kept on happening. The teachers tried to stop them.

Freddie Parker (8)

Larkrise Primary School, Great Baddow

Heroic Hermione's Adventure

Dear Diary,

Today was the best day of my life! I had gone to Hogwarts School of Witchcraft and Wizardry for the first time ever. Can you guess what house I got? Gryffindor! So did my friends, Harry and Ron. When I got to my common room, I heard a sound. Some sort of crackling sound coming from the fire in the other room. I crept over and I saw a big white globe. I went over to it and touched it and I suddenly felt really strong and like I am fully powered... My powers had awakened at last.

Amelie-Rose Bruce (9)

Larkrise Primary School, Great Baddow

Superhero

Dear Diary,

Today was the weirdest day ever! I was running around (like I do) when I fell. I thought I was okay, but I was not. I literally had wings, but I did not have a halo so I was not an angel? I thought I was a person from my favourite book, Skellig. Excitedly, I tried to fly but I could not. Probably because I hadn't practised it? When I looked in the mirror, I realised that if I had wings I had great responsibility! It dawned on me that it was my duty to save the world!

Henry Kendrick (10)
Larkrise Primary School, Great Baddow

Ronaldo

Dear Diary,

When I was younger, I was very poor. My mum worked two jobs just to get me my first pair of football boots. My mum tried to make me happy every day, but every day she was so tired. When I was younger, I always had a dream of being a professional footballer, and now I have achieved my dream. Now I play for Al Nasser, a Saudi Arabia football club. I used to play for Man United and now I have a great team and great teammates. I appreciate the support. Thank you, everyone.

Willow Murphy (9)

Larkrise Primary School, Great Baddow

Green Planet

Dear Diary,
I woke up and I was on a spaceship. Then my cat and I were on a planet. Not any old planet, it was a green planet. Then I heard a boom and a bang. A man greeted me and he said, "I can help you escape." Then he made a portal to Earth and he said, "Pay me in your youth, just eight percent of it." So now I'm back on Earth and I'm an old grandma and I can't move out of my chair, but at least I'm on Earth, but old. I feel terrible.

Lacey Richmond (8)
Larkrise Primary School, Great Baddow

Stranded On An Island

Dear Diary,

I woke up in a cage, on an island with superpowers! So, I used my super-strength to break out. Then I saw a woman on this island hiding in a bush. I went to her, she said her name was Stella. Then a man came out and I turned invisible to hide. I asked why she locked me up. She said she didn't do it but knew who had. A loud noise boomed through the island! She took me to him. He looked like a crooked old man. It was for my own good, he told me. Why...?

Oliver Ryan (9)

Larkrise Primary School, Great Baddow

The Lost Princess

Dear Diary,

I was a princess but I got lost in the woods. I had nowhere to live so I started finding some sticks and anything else to build with. It was dark and I needed to find a light to take with me. Yay, I found a light. Finally. I built a house to live in for now. I went in and started making it cosy. Suddenly, I heard some creaking noises. They were really loud. I went out of my den and started looking around. It stopped. When it stopped, I ran back into my house.

Tiana Smith (9)

Larkrise Primary School, Great Baddow

Kidnapping Tests

Dear Diary,

My sister was asleep on Chinese New Year, while I was at the parade with the rest of my family. Two days after we were asleep at home and I felt a tight zipper on my hands, then a plastic bag over my head. Me and my sister were put in a white van. I knew that because I could see through the bag. We got out and we had fake guns at our heads but then my mum walked in. It turned out my dad was testing us on what to do if we got kidnapped...

Amelia Green (10)

Larkrise Primary School, Great Baddow

Charlie's Adventure

Dear Diary,

I was walking to school and I found a shiny fifty pence, glimmering on the floor. I ran to the shop to buy a Wonka bar, and I was hoping I would strike lucky. I went into the store and I asked for a chocolate bar and I opened it and I got a... Golden Ticket! I was so happy. I ran home and told the adults. It was tomorrow, I had to get ready. Grandpa Joe said to brush my teeth, comb my hair and dust off all the mud and snow off me. Hooray!

Grace Hawkins (8)

Larkrise Primary School, Great Baddow

Patrick

Dear Diary,

I yawned and got out of bed. I said hello to SpongeBob and we went to eat some burgers and it was nice for me. I went to see if there was more food but there was no more food anywhere. I went to see our friend. Gary was gone. I went to the zoo to see some animals. I wanted to buy some, but it was too much money so I went back to see SpongeBob. Then I did something wrong. I went out of the sea and SpongeBob came. It was a crazy time.

Archie Haydon (9)

Larkrise Primary School, Great Baddow

The Little Dog

Dear Diary,

I went exploring in the forest. It was a very big forest. Then I found a cave and I explored it so that was my home. The next day, I went out and found some food and took it home. Then a little rabbit came and said hello, then ran far away. I said, "Bye," and went to bed. In the night, I heard a noise. It was just a bird. In the morning I went and explored some more. I did not see anything exciting, so I went back home.

Kaidan Wade (8)

Larkrise Primary School, Great Baddow

My Pokémon Journey

Dear Diary,

Today I was out with my Pikachu and Zygarde, looking for the legendary Pokémon Galaria Moltres in the Hoenn region, Mount Chimney. My friends came with me, Go and Chloe. We met up with some old friends and his Lucario. His fighting type would be super effective against dark-type Pokémon. We found it, but it was just a balloon. Who do we know that has balloon Pokémon? Team Rocket! Were they here to steal the legendary Pokémon? Their Pelipper released the Pokémon vending machine, out popped Pokéballs. A Melmetal and a Gyarados. We battled and won, victorious.

Rhys Jones (10)

Market Drayton Junior School, Market Drayton

My Adventure To Space

Dear Diary,

What a crazy week! A writing competition led to our class being awarded the most amazing prize! A trip into space to explore the galaxy! Crazy, right? We couldn't believe it.

After saying goodbye to my parents, we boarded the enormous aircraft. It was equipped with all the latest technology. It was so big we could've fit a whole other school inside with us.

As we took off, everyone held on so tight because of the speed we were going at. It was wild. Everyone was shocked!

Suddenly, something seemed to go wrong. Chaos. Shouting. Screaming. A crash-landing...

Olivia Davies (11)

Market Drayton Junior School, Market Drayton

The Start Of My Pokémon Journey

Dear Diary,

Yesterday was rather eventful. Mum managed to book me an air taxi to a revolutionary region called Levia. I'd heard there's been a recent discovery that can link the abilities of two Pokémon together. Anyway, once I had arrived, I noticed there was something following me. I soon recognised it as the mythical Pokémon, Meltan! I immediately threw my one and only beast ball passed down from my ancestors. *Bam!* It was caught. Instantly, I thought of the perfect name, Milkshake. Once we had bonded lots, we began to venture to the Electric Gym.

Jack Booth (11)
Market Drayton Junior School, Market Drayton

The Key

Dear Diary,

Today was amazing.

We woke in our tent, hungry. Our supplies had almost run out. It was time to go home. Packing bags to head out, we both saw it glinting in the sunlight.

"You can't do things behind my back!" Elsie snapped. We glared impatiently.

"Shut up! Look what we've found!"

We knew at once what it was - the locked secret room!

We decided we should appear at our old home, packed up our bags (although we didn't take much with us) and arrived back home. We rushed upstairs and jolted the key into the hole...

Chloe Talbot (11)

Market Drayton Junior School, Market Drayton

The Diary Of Jacob James

27th March 2023

Dear Diary,

Today I was looking on eBay for Pokémon cards until I found this Darkrai card for only twenty dollars - I clicked it without reading the reviews.

I waited for millennia until it arrived with nothing in the box apart from a letter saying, 'Get scammed'.

I hopped on eBay again and went to all his products and just left bad reviews of everything he was selling!

I looked at more Pokémon products and I saw this Pokémon card for 200,000 dollars. I clicked it like the idiot I am... not reading the reviews again!

Jacob James (11)

Market Drayton Junior School, Market Drayton

The Magical Door

Dear Diary,

Last Thursday, I moved into my new yet old house in Amsterdam, Monnickendam. The craziest thing ever happened there.

As I was heading upstairs, carrying my stuff (which was very heavy), I found a miniature door covered with faded, stained wallpaper, with worn blue dots scattered erratically.

I put my stuff down and then sliced the wallpaper away with a knife to soon realise the door was locked. I later discovered an old, rusty key that was hidden underneath an ancient-looking rug, and it matched the door's rustic colour. I went to unlock the door...

Erin Clark (11)

Market Drayton Junior School, Market Drayton

The Shocking Discovery Of Hogwarts

Dear Diary,

It has been an overwhelming, dreadful morning. You'll never believe the experience I just had! it all started when I was strolling towards the girls' toilets to read and talk to Myrtle, who was upset as usual. I noticed Harry, Hermione and Ron walk in. I was intrigued, so I went to investigate. I saw them messing with the taps but then it got rather disturbing. The fountain started to turn. Somehow, a passageway was revealed! Can you believe it, Diary, can you? I'm debating if I should confront them about the incident. Should I Diary, should I?

Jaxson Watkins (10)
Market Drayton Junior School, Market Drayton

Astronaut Saver

Dear Diary,

I went to an alien planet to save humanity from invading aliens by collecting a giant bin. I put on my spacesuit, entered the spaceship and flew to the alien planet, Zorb.

Arriving at the giant planet, I saw the bin in the distance. *I'll have to travel through the city*, I thought to myself. A problem - an alien covered with incredible armour that would be tough to sneak past.

Using a super strong potion that I had brought, I waited until he fell asleep, sneaked past and grabbed the bin.

Would it be enough to destroy them...?

Harry Bowler (10)
Market Drayton Junior School, Market Drayton

The Skyscraper Was Falling

Dear Diary,

I could never have been prepared for what was coming.

A slam on the table drew me out of my trance. "Are you listening?" I was, in fact, not listening. A shift in the ground. Shrieks of horror. The skyscraper was falling. I turned and hurtled down the spiral staircase in a panicked flurry.

My breath was quick with fear as I scrabbled through the rubble that was the third floor. I felt the building lean to the left harshly as I hurried down the flight of steps and stumbled, cursing myself under my breath.

Everything went black.

Lyla Sorbie (10)

Market Drayton Junior School, Market Drayton

The Diary Of Asher Brown

27th March 2023

Dear Diary,

I was chilling in town; a rich man came and gave me five pounds. I thanked him and ran to Quiniela Lotto. I bought a lottery ticket. Scratched it. I went from sadness to happiness in a blink of an eye.

"It's the jackpot!" I couldn't believe my eyes. I ran to the bank and cashed in the million pounds.

I bought some footballs to practise. The past weeks I've trained hard.

I got scouted for Argentina's football team and I'm about to play in the World Cup.

I'll tell you the rest later.

Kayleigh Williams (11)

Market Drayton Junior School, Market Drayton

The Missing Snow Creation

1st December 2023

Dear Diary,

You'll never guess what? The craziest thing happened to me and my brother today! We swiftly walked down an eerie archway when snowflakes gently tiptoed down from the gloomy sky and settled upon the icy pathway below. We were both overjoyed and eagerly began to shape things with the bitter-cold snow. It took us all day to build a beautiful snowman along with his snowdog. I took off my hat and scarf and placed them upon my breathtaking creation. After tea, we rushed back but they had mysteriously vanished...

Nellie McGuire (10)

Market Drayton Junior School, Market Drayton

A Pigeon Stole My Orange Plant!

November 30th 2028

Dear Diary,

Today, the next-door neighbour's pigeon stole my orange plant and they don't care about it! They didn't do anything, they didn't even reply to my mail which was sad.

But I was determined to find my orange plant no matter what challenges I would face.

I went to the pigeon loft in Pigeon Town and I discovered my orange plant.

Taking it back home, I squeezed some fresh orange juice. The next thing I knew, a dog had stolen it. I went to get it again. Something wicked had happened to the plant...

Kamil Golec (10)

Market Drayton Junior School, Market Drayton

My Dinosaur Dream

Dear Diary,

I woke up from a really strange dream. It was about a dinosaur! It was set in the Amazon rainforest. I was really happy as well as surprised. Then, I spotted a super-rare turtle-T-rex, playing with a tall herbivore (a diplodocus). Then, they ran towards the large, clear river, but then I realised that the diplodocus was helping the turtle-T-rex by helping it with her babies that had hatched. They all ran to a cascading waterfall. They then spotted a small elephant. It had lost its mother. They all met at the tall waterfall. They became friends.

Penny Davies (11)

Market Drayton Junior School, Market Drayton

The Mysterious Eye

Dear Diary,

I was camping when I heard a noise. It was the sound of branches crunching and leaves squishing. Later in the day while I was playing, I heard another strange noise. This time, it spoke. It screeched and later yelled, "Run!" It was terrifying. I've never heard anything like it. I was scared, no, petrified! Oh, and I also heard some loud screaming, so I full-on sprinted out of there. There was an oddly oversized eye watching me, making me feel nervous. "Help!" I called. My friends heard. They should have run...

Ethan Pearse (11)

Market Drayton Junior School, Market Drayton

Lupin's Day At Hogwarts

Dear Diary,

Today was chaotic. This is the reason. First, I woke up in the teacher's dorm as per usual and went to the Great Hall with the other professors and it was breakfast for the students. After breakfast, the students went to lessons and professors went to their classrooms and I was teaching DADA.

As the lesson started, I explained what we were going to do. Today I was teaching Riddikulus, and I taught them the hand movement of the spell. We began. There was a boggart, which is your biggest fear, and then Harry started to cast Riddikulus.

Finlay Gurnett (11)

Market Drayton Junior School, Market Drayton

The Tale Of The Tomb

Friday 6th October 2016

Dearest Diary,

Yesterday I had the craziest adventure of my life! What a nightmare it was! I was with all my archaeologist friends in the deserts of Ancient Egypt, hoping to find more ancient artefacts to present to the museum. We had been out there for days and days; still, we had found nothing. Nothing! I wandered over to the only patch of ground we hadn't dug up yet. I dug and I dug. My spade hit something hard. Cautiously, my team and I hauled it out. It was... Tutankhamun's tomb. The door creaked open...

Martha Cooper (10)

Market Drayton Junior School, Market Drayton

Da Wild Disaster

Dear Diary,

Wow, today was a wild one! I saw an unusual machine. I don't even know what that means! when I pressed the button saying 'Actually, don't touch', I got through to a location that I didn't recognise. I asked for directions and they explained to me. I was disappointed. I was in 'England'. What the egg even is that? I felt like I didn't fit in. I wanted to cause some mischief, but I saw a massive egg-shaped object torturing a poor citizen.

From Dawildboi, signing off. Still in a dreadful disaster.

Kyle Burton (10)

Market Drayton Junior School, Market Drayton

The Diary Of Jason Wild, Thom Taylor And Jhon James

1912, Friday 13th

Dear Diary,

On Friday, a murder happened. It happened in the middle of nowhere, in an abandoned mysterious house. The weapons that weren't used were a shotgun, a taser and a machete. Jason Wild chased Thom Taylor after the escape from the chair. On Friday the 13th, Jason came out looking for his next victim.

Jhon James was the next victim. Jason Wild put a mask on Jhon's face so he couldn't see where he was going, and Jason took him to his house and he took the mask off Jhon's face so he could see.

Tulisa Brown (10)

Market Drayton Junior School, Market Drayton

The World Of Imagination

Dear Diary,

You wouldn't believe what happened today! I fell into an imaginary world, a realm different to ours. Low gravity, strange creatures, other people like me, all stuck in infinity.

I went over and chatted to them, then became friends. Many days passed, memories made. There was one 'friend' that wasn't the same. Always jealous and very rude, always pulled pranks on the others too.

Then, one day, disaster struck. Our friend turned on us. He felt left out and wanted us to fail. So, we fought long and hard.

Lilly Bentley (10)

Market Drayton Junior School, Market Drayton

The Beast

Dear Chelsey,

I was with some friends walking home and we went into town near a forest. Suddenly, I was alone. I found myself running from something. Panting and petrified, running away from a beast, it spotted me. I had only one option - to hide. There, in front of me, was a climbable tree. Balancing on an overhanging branch, I peered through the leaves. Below me, the huge, hideous creature waited impatiently. Standing on its hind legs, clawing up at the thick branch keeping me stable. It snarled at me and the branch started to break...

George O'Sullivan (11)

Market Drayton Junior School, Market Drayton

The Amazing Diary Of Zenitsu Agatsma Demon Strength

21st December 2036

Dear Diary,

Yesterday, while the horizon was coming up, I woke up. I was having a walk to the store in butterfly mansion. When I saw Tanjiro after we had a chitchat, I said, "Bye, Tanjiro, Nezuko-Chan." On the way to my house, it happened... A pesky ol' demon jumped me! It was only a Lowermoon2 so I thought I was okay, but no, it had string art. Then he came for me. I cut his string, then used thunder dash. I stunned him. I went for it. "Full force sixfold!" I beat it. Yes.

Peace out.

Thomas Pembridge (11)

Market Drayton Junior School, Market Drayton

The Diary Of Sam Pearson

15th June 2022

Dear Diary,

It all started on the island of Lidise - a cretaceous park. I was just feeding the Pyro-raptor, and it pulled me in... I ran to the door but when I turned around, it was gone. There was nothing left. A gigantic head was barging through the window. It was a new dinosaur...

Quetzalcoatlus flew in the air and Dilophasaurus ate the employees, so I ran to the comps pen through the Giganotosaurus paddock and along the lagoon and as it was about to eat me the Mosasaurus jumped out of the water and ate it.

Sam Pearson (10)

Market Drayton Junior School, Market Drayton

Waves

Dear Diary,

Rapidly, I slipped off the gloomy grey rock. My paws landed in the sand and immediately, I turned and attempted to scramble back onto the rock. Of course, I was unsuccessful, but it was worth a shot. I glanced around. My paws were scorching in the sand. I spotted bright blue water, I pranced over, my paws sank into the sizzling sand with each swift step. Reaching the edge, I dipped my front paw into the whistling water before continuing into the singing sea. Whilst I was busy lapping up the water, a wave was on its way...

Rebecca Gledhill (11)

Market Drayton Junior School, Market Drayton

Miami Dance

Saturday 20th May 2021

Dear Diary,

It's the second day of the National Dance Competition in Miami. Khlow and I decided that since my solo wasn't until later, we could go gift shopping for our parents; we were not ready for what happened next.

I visited the perfume shop to buy something for my mum since she could not make it to nationals this year. I didn't find anything, but when I left the shop, sirens went off because Tess put the perfume in my bag and made it look like I had stolen it. Why would she do that?

Eliora Maturure (10)

Market Drayton Junior School, Market Drayton

The Incredible Journey Of Darwin Núñez

Dear Diary,

I introduced myself to the Uruguayan team as their new striker. The team consisted of two of the best players on the team, Federico Valverde and Suárez. I was so excited to play with them! My next game was due to start in two days against Korea. Then I started my training with Suárez.

On the day of the match, I was nervous but had to push through. To start the game, Suárez made a phenomenal pass to me to score. Unfortunately, I was tackled and I broke my ankle. Hopefully, I will recover soon...

Riley Sillitoe (10)

Market Drayton Junior School, Market Drayton

Magical Island

Dear Diary,

I woke up after a wonderful dream, but it was very mysterious. I was stuck on a magical island, surrounded by hundreds of shells. I was feeling nervous but also intrigued. All of a sudden, one shell began to glow all different colours like a rainbow. The shell crumbled open and the phoenix appeared above me. I felt shocked. The phoenix asked me what my wish would be. I told him I wanted to be a footballer and play for Liverpool FC. Mum shouted, "Get up, time for school!" I wonder if my dream will come true...?

Ellis Barnes (10)
Market Drayton Junior School, Market Drayton

Diary Of Heather

Monday 27th March 2023

Dear Diary,

I saw a hand grenade in a tall, mysterious man's hand. I felt immediately sick and petrified. I ran faster than I ever had before, leaving my friend (Casey) behind.

I must have run too far because when I looked back, I was lost. Great! I got up and walked around, dazed and confused. I needed to go back to check on Casey, I had to make myself become brave.

The scene was chaotic, with people trying to find their loved ones. I saw them, relief washed over me... safe and smiling!

Helena Erzincanoglu (11)

Market Drayton Junior School, Market Drayton

Pink Fluffy Unicorns

29th March, 2023

Dear Diary,

The sky is pitch-black, and the stars are bright, peaceful and lovely.

I've had a crazy week. It feels like I've travelled the world. It all started with me trekking around a rainforest and slipping on a rock. As I fell, from the corner of my eye, I spied a map.

I picked up the map and realised it could make all my dreams come true. I had to travel all the way to Spain. I opened the door of the hotel room, walked in, and saw a bridge made of light pink fluffy unicorns.

Pippa-Rose Baines (10)

Market Drayton Junior School, Market Drayton

The Diary Of Dre

9th January 2014

It started on Friday when Turkey beat France.

I was in the Turkey squad (I know I'm not starting) we were playing against Brazil. I knew it wasn't an easy game. At least I was playing with Ronaldinho (my hero). The game started 0-0 and I still hadn't been played.

Half-time started and I was subbed on. I got the ball and started a dribble, rolled past Thiago and I was through I took a power shot top left... and scored to win the World Cup. My dream came true, I was a Turkey legend!

Kasim Can (11)

Market Drayton Junior School, Market Drayton

The Monster

Wednesday 21st September, 1969
Dear Diary,
My teacher got turned into a monster and she kept getting bullied by all the older children. It was making her really upset and she wanted to get in her classroom but couldn't because all the older children were getting in her way and stopping her from getting in. She wished she could just get in her classroom but she couldn't figure a way to get there, because all the children were blocking her class because she was a monster and it was making her very angry...

Cameron (11)
Market Drayton Junior School, Market Drayton

Mario And Luigi

Dear Diary,

Today, I fought Bowser in the Mushroom Kingdom Centre. It was a tough battle. Bowser kept throwing fireballs at me and Luigi. Then, a horde of Toads came from Peach's castle. Bowser violently picked me up and threw me into a tree! Luigi used a fire flower, hitting Bowser into the tree. After, I jumped on his head like a Goomba. Then, Bowser called his army. It was Toads vs Koopas; Bowser vs me and Luigi. Bowser had had enough, picked me up and bashed me on the ground, then threw me off a tall cliff...

Charlie Redhead (10)

Market Drayton Junior School, Market Drayton

The Drawing In The Cave

4567th March 100069 Monday

Dear Diary,

Today I met a cat with two folded ears and wings. We went for a stroll and saw a cave and suddenly decided to explore it. There were many shining gems! Alan (the nickname that I gave to the cat) was shocked. He just loved crystals! We started observing them. Alan then noticed the coloured pencils on the floor. There was a drawing of a pink cat with two folded ears and wings (Alan was a blue cat). Someone was sitting and drawing and then stood up and walked away from there.

Veronika Tsymbal (11)

Market Drayton Junior School, Market Drayton

The Diary Of The Four Friends

Friday 13th October 1651

Dear Diary,

It was Halloween and we decided to go to the Halloween festival and we wanted to go into the corn maze. It was 7pm when we went in and it was scary but fun.

We had given up and tried to find our way out. It hit 3am and we were still trying, but it was like the corn maze entrance and exit had overgrown. We couldn't climb out. We passed a lot of monsters. They became alive and chased us...

If you are reading, please save us.

Ivy, Lia, Bully and Steven

Keira Lovatt (11)

Market Drayton Junior School, Market Drayton

The Day In A Life Of A Football

Dear Diary,

So it all happened on the weekend when someone played the best game they'd played in a while, the whole season in fact. I was purposefully kicked a lot that day, in and out of a net that I didn't really understand the purpose of. After that, I was kicked multiple yards away from the target. I was so high that everyone's eyes were on me. Why me? I curled better than ever. I then fell down to my death. I didn't know if I did my job correctly or not. Nobody knew. Could have hit the post.

Logan Darby (11)

Market Drayton Junior School, Market Drayton

My First Day At Hogwarts

Dear Diary,

Do you know how scared I was? Today was my first at Hogwarts. Would my family remember me? Would I get forgotten? I was super nervous. My father showed me the way to Platform 9¾. Now I was terrified. I was so confused because I couldn't see a sign anywhere saying Platform 9¾. I overheard Father saying we are going to be late. We got there and my father and mother gave me a hug, and my sis started to cry. I got on the train and waved goodbye as tears fell down my red, sad, face.

Ginny Farmer (10)
Market Drayton Junior School, Market Drayton

A Football Life

Dear Diary,

Being kicked around all day is a painful job. It all started when a mysterious man threw me onto a large green arena. There were white lines that I rolled on, I almost popped. There were several other people like me. Some were boys and some were girls, and one was my friend. He got kicked more than me. I felt bad but then he went so far that I couldn't see him. Then I got worried. I thought I would never see him again. Suddenly, I saw him in a massive crowd of people tossing him around...

Archie Jackson (10)
Market Drayton Junior School, Market Drayton

My Football Match On Sunday

Dear Diary,

On Sunday, we played against a very good team. When we started, I was on the bench and we almost scored some goals. Even our new player almost scored two goals. After, I became very happy. This match was my best match but our old striker went to CM and he was very good in his new position for the team. With two minutes left, they had scored an amazing goal. Our team was heartbroken and then a team member said we should have won the game, and our team played their best game of our good season.

Corey Timmis (11)

Market Drayton Junior School, Market Drayton

My Fairy Dream

Dear Diary,

I woke up from a wonderful dream. I lay in my bed feeling sad that it had ended. I had a dream that I was in a beautiful, mysterious garden, full of tall, green trees and a cascading waterfall. At the bottom of a tree near the waterfall, was a fairy garden. I had spoken to one of the fairies. I said, "I wish I could be a fairy." I heard my mum shouting to me. "It's time to get up!" I wonder if my fairy dream will come true and if I'll turn into a garden fairy...?

Megan Benford (10)
Market Drayton Junior School, Market Drayton

The Cat, The Fox And The Mouse

Dear Diary,

I was peacefully strolling down the path.
Something rattled in the tall grass. I looked around
and saw a ginger, furry creature. I took a closer
look and realised it was a cat! It chased me down
the long path. I ran as fast as a cheetah. I hid in a
bush. It smelled me. It pounced on me. I got
dragged, thrown and bitten! Until I got away. Then
I saw another creature! It was a big, orange
(again), furry creature. I looked up to see a
mischievous, sly fox! Then it looked down, right at
me.

Sahara Peach (10)

Market Drayton Junior School, Market Drayton

The Big Day

Dear Diary,

Today was the big day, the day where all of the demons and angels get together and fight. First, it was an angel and me. I easily won in a heartbeat. Next, it was my best friend, Death. She won, but it was harder with a more powerful angel. Then, it was an angel and an angel? I guess they had more angels than demons. Then it won. Ugh. Angel Chalices and my sister. I hated that Chalices won, but she was the strongest angel. The other round was just a blur. Next it's me and Chalices.

Heidi Stevenson (10)

Market Drayton Junior School, Market Drayton

My Dog Dexter

Dear Diary,

So, my story is amazing. It's not like I meant to ship my dog to a mystery place...

Okay, I was supposed to send a vase to China. I did that, but I also shipped my dog as well! He must have jumped in when I wasn't looking! So now I'm alone, sitting down, thinking, *what can I do?* I called the mailman, I asked, "Hello, sir, do you have my dog by any chance?" He told me that he was very sorry and that the flight to China had already left an hour ago...

Rosie-Leigh Phillips (11)

Market Drayton Junior School, Market Drayton

A Day In The Life As A Ball

Dear Diary,
I get kicked and thrown occasionally. I get kicked against a wall and if you are like me, you get kicked over a fence and threatened to be popped by our mean, old neighbour. Luckily, I rolled into a bush, so their drooling, big, scary dog didn't see me. Then, I saw another person like me. It was so round I was in love. We became friends. We visited the park together. One day, we were at the park. We were on the swings till two boys took her away nastily. Will I see her ever again?

Declan Bonell (10)
Market Drayton Junior School, Market Drayton

The Best Day Of My Life

Dear Diary,

What an amazing day I've had! I went to Old Trafford to watch Manchester United play. A couple of hours before the match, I walked to the shop and bought a scarf. Then I placed my scarf on the bench beside us to take a picture in front of the stadium. I turned my head for one second and suddenly my scarf was gone. I think I know what was going on. Someone had stolen my new scarf. As I looked up, I saw a tall shadow towering over me. It was my number one player, Marcus Rashford...

Amber Lloyd (10)

Market Drayton Junior School, Market Drayton

My Strange Adventure

Dear Diary,
What a chaotic day I've had. My friend and I were having a sleepover when we noticed a light outside of the window! Before we thought of anything, we ran outside and followed the light into a snowy forest. Then we found a rusty locked gate; we tried to climb over it, but it was far too high! We grabbed some dead wood and leaned it against the gate. Then we crept on the log and got inside! Someone called my phone. I picked it up and saw it was Grandma and she told me to come home.

Sophie Hill (10)

Market Drayton Junior School, Market Drayton

Treasure

Friday 21st September, 1969
Dear Diary,
I lost my football in a forest and went looking for it.
Tangled up in the tall trees, I spotted a skeleton. In his hand, I found a map. I looked. It had a cross. It looked like a treasure map.
I followed where it said to go. There was a fly trap. It had an animal trapped inside it.
I ran in the direction of the cross and saw a massive creature the size of a mountain. I sprinted as quick as a flash. It was still chasing me. I tripped...

Liam Randall (10)
Market Drayton Junior School, Market Drayton

The Diary Of The Amazing Comeback Of Josh!

21st July 2023

Dear Diary,

Yesterday, you wouldn't believe it. I got dressed in my football kit and got my shin pads on. I put my boots on, got in the car and went to Greenfield. At half-time I was exhausted, 3-0 down. I got subbed off, then came back on and got a goal, but just as I was about to score, I got tackled and awarded a pen. I scored the rebound. 2-3, one more minute, in the box... hit the crossbar. Then I scored, 3-3. Then it went to pens for us to win the magnificent cup.

Josh McGuinness (11)

Market Drayton Junior School, Market Drayton

The Diary Of Puerto Fragrant

31st October 2023

Dear Diary,

It was Halloween night when I saw a man looking at me from my backyard.

I didn't feel safe, so I grabbed a kitchen knife and hid.

He broke in with an axe and started chopping the living room door down. As soon as he found me, I stabbed him!

I made a run for the door and quickly made a trap whilst he was recovering from the wound. When he got up, he charged at me with the axe in his hand. A paint tub swung from the door and knocked him out.

Hadley Orwell (11) & Bobby Allen (11)

Market Drayton Junior School, Market Drayton

The Mysterious Attic

March 1st 2011

Dear Diary,

I strolled through the front door. I was so happy to come home to my dog until I heard a thud in the attic. I was determined to find out what was waiting for me. It was only my friend and me, but we decided to face our fears, so we both walked up the stairs in terror. I found us a ladder to climb up.

After about thirty seconds, we were up, but both of us couldn't turn back...

We were trapped. We couldn't escape.

What would we find within?

Minnie Johnson (10)

Market Drayton Junior School, Market Drayton

The Key Of The Water

Tuesday, August 11th, 1945

Today, Gibbs told me of an ancient key of which an old pirate had lived to tell the tale. It was told that whoever held it was able to unlock their innermost precious desires in life, and I have to have it. Imagine the power it holds.

But the problem is that the pirate who is currently in possession is a captain who Hell itself spat right out. As soon as I was able to walk out of the bar, somebody called my name. A familiar voice from the past - Jack Sparrow...

Poppy Williams (11)

Market Drayton Junior School, Market Drayton

New Football Team

Dear Tigers,

My new football team introduced me to everyone in the new team.

We played at Telford behind a restaurant in a park. Everyone in the team was excited to have me with them. In the second half, I had my first shot but hit the post. Then Corey had a shot and 'skied' it.

I got to play the whole match and flick the ball in the air. I took every corner and free kick. I was second place for Man of the Match. On the way home, I had a McDonald's that I did not want.

Joshua Howson (10)

Market Drayton Junior School, Market Drayton

The Day I Bucked

Dear Diary,

Yesterday, I felt a mixture of feelings. I met someone new! It was so exciting; I didn't think she would come back after what I did that day. It was in the emerald-green grass we could see all over the small town. It was my dream come true, but as we started to walk away from the scorching sun, she kicked my stomach. It was so painful. I ignored it but then it became worse. As I continued, the pain spread on top of my back so I started to buck. I never wanted to hurt her.

Georgina Bussue (11)

Market Drayton Junior School, Market Drayton

The Diary Of Ellie Write

20th July 2017

Dear Diary,

It's me again. I think I had the worst fall in history! As you know, I have my own house, my own horse and my own stables.

I live in England; I am terrified and shell-shocked to go back on my horse (Jasper).

I am so lucky that I had my best friend Ruby by my side when I fell. She gave me advice, and she explained, "To be a good rider, you need to fall off at least seven times. Learn from your mistakes." It was the best advice ever!

Eve Morris (11)

Market Drayton Junior School, Market Drayton

The Diary Of Tigers

Dear Diary,

We had just beaten PSG in the semis.

The headlines were Tigers vs Man City (I knew I wasn't going to start). It began. It was an intense first half, ending 3-3. Chance after chance, then came the 89th minute. I came on. It was the 94th minute and we got a corner. I was on the edge, waiting for the ball. One mistake by the defence. It came to one shot and scored. Goal! The final whistle blew.

Tigers, champions of Europe Champions.

Yours,

Alfie Bailey.

Alfie Bailey (11)

Market Drayton Junior School, Market Drayton

Clay Pigeon Champion

4th of April 2023

Dear Diary,

Today I went to a BASC clay pigeon competition with my nanny, grandad and brother. I was doing great in my lesson before my competition and soon it was my turn to shoot. I was doing really well. I was the best there.

It was the final shot, me against a professional. I was so excited but nervous at the same time because he was so good.

It was his turn; he missed. It was my turn now, I hit it! I was the winner - I had won the competition.

Edward Pomfret (10)

Market Drayton Junior School, Market Drayton

I Accidentally Shipped My Dog To Africa!

Dear Diary,

I accidentally shipped my dog to Africa.

Like I said, I was sad, but I had to find him. I couldn't cancel the shipment, so I ran to the post office, but he wasn't there. I didn't know where to go now. I was lost. I didn't know what to do, but I heard a bark. It was in a box. It fell out of the van. I opened it. Was it him? I hoped in excitement. It was a speaker. There was a note and it said, 'I have your dog!'

Why would they have him?

Taylor Hogan (11)

Market Drayton Junior School, Market Drayton

The Diary Of Charlie

13th April 2012

Dear Diary,

I was benched. It was a tight game on the final whistle. It was still 0-0 and the gaffer said I was coming on for extra time and it went to pens. I took the last one. I was shaking, what if I missed? It was 4-4. France missed their last pen and it was my time to have a shot. If I scored, we would be world champions.

I got the ball to take the pen against Hugo Lloris. I was going to score bottom right. I stepped up, I scored. World Champions!

Ellis Jones (11)

Market Drayton Junior School, Market Drayton

The Day In The Life Of A Fish

Dear Diary,
As I awoke from my slumber, diving as usual out in the rough Atlantic sea, swerving between the rocks. I met my friends and then I met a squid, so I swerved around him. I was as happy as could be. Then I met a school of fish and a starfish diving. Then I caught up with a dolphin, but then I had to say goodbye. I drifted around a corner and swam past all my friends. The starfish stole my grin but then I stole it back and swam back but then something bad happened...

Matilda Chapman (10)
Market Drayton Junior School, Market Drayton

The Diary Of Ruby White

15th August 2021

Dear Diary,

It's me. I fell off my horse - again! But it was worse than usual. I wouldn't go back on (Rolo) my horse. I live in England, I have my own house. I also have my own stables opposite my house.

My leg was very painful after the fall. I broke it! I'm so lucky that my friend Ellie came to help me. She said, "To be a good rider, you need to fall off at least five times." I am lucky to have her. My best friend!

Carys Higginson (10)

Market Drayton Junior School, Market Drayton

The Sleepover

Dear Diary,

What an extremely fun day I have had. I went to my bestie's house for a sleepover, then we went to go and grab snacks for a midnight feast. Later that day, her mum took us to McDonald's and then we went to go rollerskating. It was really fun. I got the hang of it at the end. After, we had a break, so we played some tennis. Obviously, Megan won and later we went home and listened to music and had our midnight feast. There were dozens of tasty snacks. OMG!

Evelyn Griffiths (10)

Market Drayton Junior School, Market Drayton

The Diary Of David

21st June 2024

Dear Diary,

The last few weeks have been unreal. This is how it started. I got a call from an unknown number and unusually, I answered it. I would've normally left it, had I not felt like answering it. It was Southgate, yes, I couldn't believe he said I was in the team for the Euros.

It was a tough match, but I had an okay game. It was the last minute. I scored the winner. I'm a national hero. We were the best country in Europe. David.

Oscar Donnelly (11)

Market Drayton Junior School, Market Drayton

My Diary

Dear Diary,

Something unforgettable has happened to me! Tomorrow is my birthday, but sadly, no one has responded to my invites until now! My brother (Jacob) is back from prison (he went over the speed limit) but he loves me more than anything and now he has proved it... When no one came to my birthday, he secretly realised the date was wrong so he made brand-new invites and made sure to put the right dates on them, and everyone came and then we all had a brilliant time.

Emilia Sloan (8)

Market Drayton Junior School, Market Drayton

Dear Diary

Today was an eventful day... I lost track of Zelda, but the Ritos from Rito village told me that they had seen her ride past on her beautiful white horse not that long ago. I found her on the peak of a nearby cliff. She was trying to find a way into a sealed shrine but could not get inside. When she heard me riding up the cliff, she looked enraged to see me and took her anger out on me, telling me that she did not need a knight and that she was the only one with a brain.

Max Tweddle (11)

Market Drayton Junior School, Market Drayton

My Brother Ruins Beach Day

Dear Diary,

I walked on the warm sand. A hot breeze blew past me as I found a space to make a ginormous sandcastle. I put sand in the bucket and tapped it down and flipped it over. Sadly, it didn't work; I tried again and it worked! I made many more of them. There were some ups and down but I made it. But then I needed some water for a small pond. I got some from the ocean. I admired my work. My smelly brother and his friend were near and they ran it over! No!

Isabelle Cadman-Reed (10)

Market Drayton Junior School, Market Drayton

The Mysterious Island

Dear Diary,

Last night, I found a mysterious island where big animals are small and small animals are big. I weirdly rode a massive bee! Would you believe that, Diary? I was also pooped on by a crazy bird, but nobody wants to know that! I also saw an immensely big spider. I got trapped in its horrible, silky web. Its fangs were massive! I found out that colossal ants were tearing down trees. Ants. I couldn't believe it!

Erin Parton (10)

Market Drayton Junior School, Market Drayton

Pokémon Adventure

Dear Diary,

Today was crazy! I caught a Pidgeotto, it was amazing but hard and Team Rocket tried to take Pikachu! Metapod got injured fighting Pidgeotto. But suddenly, Team Rocket and Meowth appeared and third to take Pikachu! They woke Beedrils, so we hid in a cabin and waited for them to leave. We left the cabin and went to the Kacuna Tree to get Metapod, but something happened that was eventful and venturesome...

Riley Smith (11)
Market Drayton Junior School, Market Drayton

Diary Of A Footie Boy

Dear Diary,

I had the best day ever. Today, I woke up with a burst of energy and jumped out of bed. When I finished my daily routine, I went to play football. I didn't really like my ball that much so I asked my mum, "Please can you get me a new football and new football gloves?" Weirdly, she accepted and bought me the things. It was expensive, but she bought them. I started playing better and trained more. Then later, a scout came to our training and said that I would get a trial. So now I'm waiting.

Peter Ntereba (8)

New Hall School, Boreham

My Worst Day Ever!

Dear Diary,

Today was the worst day ever, the WDE for short. The school bullies bullied me repeatedly and even put me in the bin! Today I had dance at lunch and couldn't eat the delicious chocolate doughnut which was only served today. Then I got told off for being late for class. At break, everything was fine until the disgraceful bullies came again. I kicked them all and got told off and got a red card. When I came home, I argued for a long hour and got sent straight to bed! Such a bad day today! Ugh! Bye!

Amelia Craven (8)

New Hall School, Boreham

A Day In The Life OF Bligh

Dear Diary,

When I was a baby, I was chubby and cute and I used to sleep a lot. My daddy would throw me in the air so high that I once hit my head on the moon. My family told me that when I grew up, I would become an astronaut. Later through my baby years, I got a job working for NASA where I worked my way up to chief pilot and was awarded the best-ever rocket kid in the whole galaxy. This is in the Book of World Records and my next stop is the planet, Mars.

Bligh Middleton (6)
New Hall School, Boreham

Miss Time Traveller

Dear Diary,

Today was the most incredible day of my life! I discovered a time machine in my grandpa's shed. I couldn't believe my eyes. It was a small metal box with lots of buttons and levers. Without a second thought, I pressed the button marked, 'Go'. In a flash, I was transported back in time to the era of dinosaurs! I saw a huge T-rex and gigantic brachiosauruses. It was like nothing I'd ever seen before. After exploring for hours, I pressed the button to return home and found myself back in the shed. I couldn't wait to tell!

Covenant Ali (10)

Oxford Education Centre, Cowley

My Magnificent Day

Dear Diary,

Today was one of my best and worst days ever. I scored a banging bicycle kick against Juventus. My legs were like lightning. I sprinted in a flash to the corner and shouted, "Suii!" The Juventus fans started to throw banana peels at me. My teammate Pepe came and celebrated with me, and the fans threw a plastic water bottle at his head. He got very angry and chucked it back at them. I told them to shush. Quickly getting the ball and darting down the field, I scored a beautiful goal. I winked at the Juventus fans.

Mohammed Ibrahimi (10)

Oxford Education Centre, Cowley

Iced Scream

Today was the worst day of my life because my best friend broke her arm. We were so excited to go ice skating. Even though the enormous queue was so long. Let me tell you how she broke her arm. We got onto the slippery ice but Ann-May didn't know how to skate. I decided to help her because I had been skating for a while. I was holding her hand tightly but then lost grip and she fell straight onto her arm with a *boom!* The racing ambulance arrived at the ice rink and rushed Ann-May to the hospital.

Tamzin Sibanda (10)
Oxford Education Centre, Cowley

The Boy With Wings

Today I saw an apple. It was bright red and it looked crunchy. I took a bite and suddenly, wings appeared from my shoulder blades! The wings flapped and flapped and I flew all the way to Paris and saw the Eiffel Tower. People thought I was a strange bird and they pointed at me. Then I flew to the highest mountain and sat at the top like an eagle. I saw lots of clouds and it was super foggy. Finally, I flew back home because I was hungry. I ate spaghetti with cheese for dinner and I love it.

Ruwa Musiyarira (7)
Oxford Education Centre, Cowley

The Bad Day

Dear Diary,

Today I was on my way to school when all of a sudden, there were policemen after me! Abruptly, they came and arrested me for no reason! I said, "I am just a child going to school. I haven't done anything wrong!" but unexpectedly, they said I wasn't a child and I was crazy for thinking I was! Just then, I realised that my backpack for 'schoolwork' was full of the missing jewels from the palace! I was stealing! Soon, we were at the station and I was in jail! I hope this is just a dream...

Faye Wellock (11)

Park Primary School, Colne

Bob The Giant

Dear Diary,
I woke up fifty feet in the air. My bed seemed like an ant. I had to know how this happened. I tried to shrink, but I just kept growing. I slept all day. It was almost midnight! what would happen if it went midnight? I had millions of questions! I have twelve minutes. I had to be average height or what would happen? I'm shaking, I'm in space. The moon and Earth are fun to spin around. I'm panicking, it's five minutes till midnight. Four minutes, three minutes, two minutes, one minute...

Kacie Singleton (11)
Park Primary School, Colne

Sticky Disaster

Dear Diary,

Today I went on a school trip. Firstly, I went to the toilet, but there was a huge queue. So I decided to wait my turn. But when I got out, the coach was gone... I went into the kitchen and ate *all* the pudding! It was the best moment of my life. But then I realised the security cameras were watching over me. I tried to get rid of the evidence but it was too late. They had come back and I was sat in the headteacher's office, eating the kitchen's pudding...

Emily James (11)
Park Primary School, Colne

The Girl Who Disappeared

Dear Diary,

Today I went on a school trip called 'The Shakespeare', which was all about the history of the old times in 1564. I decided I needed to go to the toilet, but there was no one there, which was surprising. I shut the door but all of a sudden, the lights turned off which was super creepy, and the next thing I knew, I was sucked up into another strange dimension with people who grew horns on top of their heads.

Shilo Butcher (11)

Park Primary School, Colne

Diabetic-Free Phoebe

Dear Diary,

This morning I went to find my machines and they went missing. After, I went to ask my mother and she had no clue...

I was at school and it felt so weird. I was as free as a bird, I didn't need to test my blood sugars at break and dinner. I just went straight outside!

I'm about to go to bed right now. I hope to live like this forever.

Phoebe Daffern (11)

Park Primary School, Colne

Bogart's Favourite Hobby!

Dear Diary,

Today I woke up at 6:17 exactly. I jumped down from the tree in the back garden. I tried to find my way down but it was hard (because it was eighteen feet tall!). Finally, I got down and went through the emerald cat flap! I live in a pea-sized cottage, it may sound quite small and cramped, but my owner's so rich and buys me everything made out of gold, diamonds, or emerald! The food she gets me is so yummy! I love my owner and give her cuddles, but my favourite thing is chasing the mailwoman!

Rowan McNamara (9)

Priorsford Primary School, Peebles

Sally's Fish!

Dear Diary,

Today I woke up at 6:15, which is kinda late! I decided I wanted some food, so I went downstairs and (as I had practised) opened the fridge. Then I smelt it. Fishy. Sweet. Delicious. I instinctively sniffed it out and dragged it onto the floor. I started to eat it. It was *so* yummy! I realised it was salmon, my favourite! For the rest of the day after that, I slept (most of the time!), ate, prowled the house and relaxed. I felt brilliant! Another day being the queen of the house! I always will be!

Edith Wardman (10)

Priorsford Primary School, Peebles

A Day In The Life Of Cian Wilson

Dear Diary,

I was playing football one sunny morning with my friends when it all went black! I woke up in a helicopter with my friends. We were all tied to chairs. Then a very mysterious, black figure walked into the same room as us. He spoke in a very deep voice, like a robot. He said that we were nearly at our destination and would be landing soon. We were going to a deserted island in Alaska. When we got there, I swear I saw something like one hundred monkeys with bows and arrows. We were terrified and starving!

Cian Wilson (10)

Priorsford Primary School, Peebles

Pedro's Diary (Top Secret)

Hi! I'm Pedro and this is my (top secret) diary! Thursday: So I woke up as usual at exactly eight o'clock in the morning, and then I realised... I had a flight at nine! So I got dressed as fast as I could! I ran, no, walked, down the stairs (I wasn't risking breaking my leg). I grabbed a bowl of my favourite cereal 'Crusty Cornflakes' and then I realised I felt like crying and on top of that, my shirt was back to front. I tried to change it back but I fell and now I'm covered in cornflakes!

Harrison Laidlaw (10)

Priorsford Primary School, Peebles

How I Got Eaten By A Bear In The Champions League Final

It was ten minutes till the game starts. Everyone was nervous because it was the Champions League final, Liverpool vs Manchester United. The game started and in the tenth minute, I scored a banger in the top bins to make it 1-0. The game started again and Manchester United almost scored. But the goalie saved it and we almost scored. But, on the sixty-fourth minute, a bear came on the pitch and ate me. I was very scared, very scared. It was disgusting in the bear. But the bear coughed and I came out of the bear.

Holly Clark (10)
Priorsford Primary School, Peebles

Cookie's Meals

Dear Diary,

Today I woke up at 5:45am to do my daily stuff. I started by having my four-course tuna and mayonnaise salad with a touch of salt but no pepper. Once I finished it, I plodded down to the beach to have a swim. I got back to my small cottage and had lunch. Then I did some yoga and had a cat nap. Oops. I slept in. Then I had supper and watched TV and ate ice cream then I went to bed and had a bad dream, ate some more, then went back to bed.

Isobel Robertson (10)

Priorsford Primary School, Peebles

The Weirdest Day

Dear Diary,

Today the strangest thing happened. I was taking my casual walk when I saw a rabbit hole. It wasn't normal. It was shaped like a star. I decided to go in this magical, time-travelling thing. I told you that because it really was. I jumped in like a kangaroo, and then a golden, gleaming light shone. It looked like the party I had when I was five. I couldn't believe this was happening. Then it fell silent. Just that second I heard nothing. I saw a tiny hopping rabbit that was wearing a watch, hat and suit...

Marley Wye (10)
Rolleston Primary School, Glen Parva

Iga And Her Life!

Dear Diary,

In Poland, there lived a dog who was always excited. The dog's name was Iga and I am her! It was Sunday. As I went to my bed, the new day came. As I opened my eyes, everything became blurry and my owners went shopping. As they came back to me, I could smell them so I barked but I did not notice but I was barking at a wall! Then I was playing with my ball but I bit my owner but it wasn't on purpose. I am worried what will happen next in my puzzled life!

Amelia Jedrzejczyk (9)

Rolleston Primary School, Glen Parva

My Christmas Trip To Thailand

Dear Diary,

I just got back from two weeks in Thailand. It was magical to see so many animals on the trip. My family went to an elephant sanctuary where we saw old elephants. We also saw tiger cubs. They were so soft and sleepy. We went to see some cool dolphins. I loved it. We also saw a big Buddha statue. It was taller than my house. I loved swimming in the nice and warm sea! I saw my uncle, his name is Uncle Mat. I went on the big, scary slides! For dinner I had BBQ fish.

Ethan Wilson (6)

St Bernadette Catholic Primary School, London Colney

The Cooked Dragon

Dear Diary,

Today was a magical day. I saw a beautiful enchanted castle. In the castle was a big, fierce dragon. The dragon was having a big nap. He was blowing smoke out of his nostrils. I went up to him and said, "Wakey, wakey, dragon." He was very upset and tried to turn me into a roast chicken. I was running away from the dragon. I started to battle with a sword. Guess what I'm having for tea - a cooked dragon!

Penny Pattison (6)
St Bernadette Catholic Primary School, London Colney

The Day I Stole The Princess' Diary

Dear Diary,

Princess Wanda's diary is cursed! A day ago, I stumbled upon Princess Wanda's sparkling diary. In curiosity, I paused and stared at it. *Make up your mind*, I thought to myself, until I saw Wanda come towards me. Moments later, I arrived home when the book started glittering to catch my attention. I opened it up and every single word shone. It was written in glimmer pen! At that moment, I knew Wanda's diary wasn't some ordinary diary. I wrote a quick summary of my day but what would the consequences be? Wanda's diary will be claimed mine!

Daniella Mudizo (10)

St Margaret's Lee CE Primary School, Lewisham

Dear Diary

Last night, my sister Artemis went on an adventure to Greece. She was looking for more followers, particularly girls under seven, with no interest in love. This would be to avoid the girls leaving her on their search for love. Hiding behind a tree, Artemis found a boy who asked to join her. "That's a problem because I swore I would never let another boy join after what happened before!" However, the boy promised he had no interest in love but loved hunting. But the lost boys who joined broke their promise. Artemis allowed him, but I, Apollo, killed him!

Elijah (9)

St Margaret's Lee CE Primary School, Lewisham

Diary Of A Mr Knapp

Dear Diary,

Today was a terrible day. George and Harold dropped a huge water bomb so I gave them a shove, but then I remembered Melvin in the future was headteacher. So future Melvin and normal Melvin kicked me out of the school. I knew I couldn't do anything else, so I went to the avocado store and bought millions of avocadoes and made myself a guacamole bath, but I covered it with glass and got some anchovies, but I made sure the guacamole was warm and then, "Aah!" I felt like I made the right choice. "Yes!"

Anirudh Pritila (9)

St Mary's CE Junior School, Old Basing

A Snowflake's Life

Dear Diary,

My life started as boring water vapour floating rapidly in a gentle, white cloud. Every day was ordinary, and I was ordinary, as well as the others, but I still didn't fit in. All the water vapours I cared for transformed into crystal-clear snowflakes. It had been many years without winter weather, which means no snowflakes! Suddenly, the air turned cold, magical snow was falling and so was I! Once I fell, I joined many friends on a blanket of snow. Diary, this is me telling you to be a superhero with resilience.

Nora Grewal (9)

St Mary's CE Junior School, Old Basing

Dear Diary

On Saturday, it was an unusual but cool weekend as I had a fantastic sleepover with my friend and it was my birthday! I received some presents that I got to open. I was jubilant as we got to watch 'Turning Red' which was amazing. Although I didn't get enough sleep, we had so much fun!
Before we slept, I had my birthday party! I felt excited and I also felt I was in a birthday mood. Interestingly, we had cupcakes instead of cake. What a day it was! But in the night, we filled our mums' shoes with rocks.

Emma Shahini (8)

St Mary's CE Junior School, Old Basing

The Diary Of An Incredible Snowflake

Dear Diary,

I woke up this morning and dropped down from the cloud. I frowned. I am fed up with being a snowflake. I don't want to be a snowman and I hate being someone's snowball. Last year I was squashed by a car tyre. I turned brown. Yuck! I can't stand it. I-I-I... won't be snow. I hate being snow. I guess I have to bear it. It is *so* boring. After a while, you melt. I'm now on the ground, waiting for someone to throw me from the garden and into the trees. Being snow is actually fun.

Isaac Hampton (9)

St Mary's CE Junior School, Old Basing

Dear Diary

I had the best sleepover yesterday. I went to my BFF Ivan's house. We played lots of fun games like 'FIFA 18' on the PS4. I played as Real Madrid and he Barcelona. I won 3-2. I like to think I did better than him (but don't tell him that). Later, we played some outdoor games, built an amazing fort and watched a movie before bed. Best sleepover ever! I also had a great time in Morroco. I rode a camel, went hiking to the Atlas Mountains. We stayed at a beautiful resort and spent our time in the pool.

Kiaan Iyer (9)

St Mary's CE Junior School, Old Basing

The Secret Life Of A Snowflake

Dear Diary,

Today I fell out of a cloud as a snowflake. It was very petrifying and sort of fun. Although I was very high above the ground, I still travelled slowly. When I got to the ground, I was scrunched up into a snowball and thrown at someone's head and then I crumpled to the ground. I was rolled into a snowman and was cold. After that, a massive orange stick (carrot) was pushed in my face and stayed there until a little child came along. Soon, I melted and went back to the clouds and it happened again.

Joshua Porter (9)
St Mary's CE Junior School, Old Basing

A Snowflake's Life

Dear Diary,

Today was the most exhilarating day ever. I turned into a snowflake. I was so happy because I got joined with all my friends and family. Then I started to fall. Yep, you heard me, fall. It was so slow though. Then I had a well-deserved nap. Surprisingly comfortable. I slept for *ages*, and then I woke up and had a chat with Isaac. Then I hit the ground with a *thud*. It hurt a bit. Then I was turned into a snowman. It was so fun but I missed Isaac the snowflake. Bye.

James Croxon (9)

St Mary's CE Junior School, Old Basing

Dear Diary

At the weekend, I went to London... yay! It was very busy. I was in the queue. Luckily, it wasn't that long. The man was checking a man's bag and he had a Japanese egg frying pan in his bag... how funny!

There was an amazing Chinese town with lanterns in the beautiful sky. We watched a magician escapologist. He tried to escape from a straitjacket and a chain in under two minutes. He had four seconds left before he escaped. This was all in central London I think.

We went to M&M's World.

Emmy King (9)
St Mary's CE Junior School, Old Basing

Stagecoach Day

Last weekend, I happily went to Stagecoach. I go there every Saturday. At Stageccoach, my kind friends and I did some singing and acting. We were going to do a show! It's Aladdin, so we had to learn all the songs in Aladdin and that took a very long time. To relax, we went to play a game called 'Splat'. I didn't win! After that, we went to eat our snacks. They were really yummy. Finally we went downstairs for a re-run of the whole show. It was great and I enjoyed it. Then it was time to go home!

Janella Adeliyi (9)
St Mary's CE Junior School, Old Basing

The Incredible Diary Of A Snowflake

Dear Diary,

1:30am exactly, I was in the cloud. I am water vapour. It was so cold in the sky and clouds, I started to freeze. Then, I started to fall from the sky. My brother was following me. I started to form into a beautiful, crystal-clear snowflake and a lot more snowflakes were coming down, plummeting quite quickly. As soon as I hit the ground, a lightning-fast group of kids came over and played with me. They made snow angels, and snowmen and had a snowball fight. The team I was on won the game!

Stanley Holmes (8)
St Mary's CE Junior School, Old Basing

The Incredible Diary Of A Snowflake

Dear Diary,
Today I might be able to fall down so then people can build snowmen, and snowballs and go sledging. Then my dad said that it was time to go. I was very nervous to jump off the grey, furious clouds. Suddenly, someone pushed me off. Anyway, it was so scary that I was screaming. When I got to the ground, people were asleep because I think it was 12pm. When it was the morning, people came running outside to play in the snow. I was in a fight with another person and we won. I was so happy.

Lexi Berry (8)
St Mary's CE Junior School, Old Basing

The Game Of Goodness

Dear Diary,

The Fortnite update happened. New weapons called the Kinetic Katana and the Mythic Havoc Shotgun. I only use a Tac Pistol med kit and med spray, a Kinetic Katana and a Havoc Pump Shotgun.

You find the Havoc Pump Shotgun in a vault or there is a massive rift which is a portal and an island comes out of it. There are zip wires, and at the top, there is a flag and you have to capture it before anyone else does. But if someone gets it first, you have to get them, so you can have it.

Jacob Bolger (9)

St Mary's CE Junior School, Old Basing

A Day In The Life Of A Snowflake

Dear Diary,
Today was a very exciting day for my brother and me because it was 3am and I was starting my day as water vapour. All of a sudden, it got so cold. I was starting to freeze. I was free. I was starting to fly through the atmosphere. My parents always told me this day would come, so I wasn't excited or worried. I was scared. I needed my brother, but he had gone the opposite way. Before long, I was with all the others on the ground, waiting like a white blanket. Waiting for children.

Ella Head (9)
St Mary's CE Junior School, Old Basing

The Incredible Diary Of A Snowflake

Dear Diary,

Today was fantastic because it snowed for the first time. I plummeted to the ground. Soon, I would be a part of the white blanket of snow. I kept getting trodden on by thousands of kids. Suddenly, I got vigorously grabbed by a kid and went from house to house. I got put into a snowman. An old man looked out and muttered to himself, "I wish I had kids." He saw loads of families having a great time. *Poor man,* I thought. But the next day, we all went back to the sky.

Jax Flood (9)

St Mary's CE Junior School, Old Basing

A Snowflake

Dear Diary,

Today was an extraordinary day. At 4am, I started my journey as water vapour. Suddenly, I began to freeze! I was flying. I was scared to be a snowflake. I was having lots of fun but I was freezing. I fell on the ground from the sky and my friends came from the sky. I was happy but I was exhausted by coming from the sky to the ground. I was so excited because I want to be someone's snowman and snow angel. I hope everyone can have fun with me and my friends and make a snowman.

Saanvi Mahika (9)

St Mary's CE Junior School, Old Basing

The Incredible Diary Of A Snowflake

Dear Diary,

Today was an exhausting day! I was lying down in a water puddle as my parents were wide awake. Suddenly, as soon as I got up, I was freezing cold but my parents were fine. I began to freeze. I thought I was about to die. Suddenly, I felt like I was free and I was flying as a snowflake. I couldn't wait to be part of a snowball fight or a snowman. After a while, I noticed that I wasn't the only one who was excited, my gloomy parents were too. They were so excited as well.

Siri Rikka (9)
St Mary's CE Junior School, Old Basing

The Same Life Snowflake

Dear Diary,
Today was my thirty-first day of falling from the sky and I'm sick of it! Every single day I go to the same place and I'm used for the same thing. Today I prayed to be used for something else, like a snowman or a snowball fight, not just a snow angel or being squashed. As I fell from the sky, I froze with shock as I saw I was one of the first snowflakes because I'm usually one of the late ones. I couldn't wait for what I was going to be used for. Wish me luck.

Elizabeth O'Leary (8)
St Mary's CE Junior School, Old Basing

The Incredible Snowflake Diary

Dear Diary,

It was 2pm and I was sitting in the soft clouds. I was going to have an exhilarating day because I was going to form into a snowflake and slowly fall down. I was starting to form quickly because of how cold it was. I saw lots of other snowflakes forming. I fell as fast as a car on the motorway. I was excited because I might turn into a snowman, or snow angel or be in a snowball fight, but I was scared as well. I had hit some snow. Everyone was awake. People played with us.

James Condliffe (8)
St Mary's CE Junior School, Old Basing

The World Of Imagination!

Dear Diary,

Guess what I dreamt of? It was crazy! First, I walked into a big, blue and pink cloud with brown wooden gates. It wasn't any ordinary cloud, it floated in the direction you ordered it to. It was also filled with candy and chocolate and all sorts of other sweets!

It all started on a sunny day. A very purple sunsetting day. I was happy to say there were butterflies and flowers all over the place!

I also feel very, very comforted because my friends are with me.

Iniya Sasikumar (9)

St Mary's CE Junior School, Old Basing

The Weird Sleepover...

A few months ago, my friend and I went to Charis' house (my other friend) for a sleepover. It was very funny and unusual. After our parents left, the second bed had been placed next to me and Charis' bed. We played a very strange game named 'Octy Game'. Since I had placed some of my stuffies in my bag, they were some of the characters in the game. We played the adventure for about two hours until one of our friends got very sleepy, so then we had to close the game down.

Alicia Ng (9)
St Mary's CE Junior School, Old Basing

The Amazing Diary Of A Snowflake

Dear Diary,

Today was a very stressful day. Lots of people tried to step on me. I was crystal clear. I hated it. I fell down the sky, 40,000 miles down. I was really scared. "Hi," someone said. They were acting like I was their own child. I tried to move around but they kept on running towards me. I let them take me where they wanted to take me. But then they took me to a garbage truck. I was so confused, but they had a health kit to help me... Bye-bye! Bye...!

Harlie Kipping (8)

St Mary's CE Junior School, Old Basing

The Snowflake's Fall

Dear Diary,

Today was the most breathtaking day of my life. I was falling from my fluffy cloud down to the hard ground! I could feel my body freezing up. My arms became frozen sticks with crystal-clear ice shards sticking out. My legs became these ice lollies with twisted frozen tentacles wrapping around them. I was about to hit the ground. "Argh!" I cried, and with a quiet *thunk*, I was a white, cold snowflake, happily lying on the cold ground.

Thomas Baldwin (9)
St Mary's CE Junior School, Old Basing

Chapter Four, Season Two

Dear Diary,

It was a big day for me because, on 10th March, it was chapter four, season two. I updated Fortnite and hopped on joyfully as ever. I saw the trailer and saw cars could drift and bikes could do damage to players and yourself, so I made sure I was careful on the bikes. After a bit of the trailer, I saw these rails you could grind on which was so cool, and you could also do tricks on them. I couldn't believe my eyes when I saw the battle pass skins.

Eshan Golleru (9)

St Mary's CE Junior School, Old Basing

The Circus

Dear Diary,

My BFF Isla and I went to the circus together, and it was so much fun. Also, my mum was there supervising us and my brother went too. It was on a field. We really enjoyed it. There was a man on super high monkey bars doing flips and even standing on top of them. Also, there was a man who was incredibly strong and I could tell because he was holding a lady by his pinky! It was incredible. I couldn't believe it. I had the best time ever!

Mia-Lee Kerrigan (9)

St Mary's CE Junior School, Old Basing

The Circus Is Amazing

Dear Diary,
My BFF Mia and I and her mum went to the fair at a field at Jay Miller's Circus. Mia and I felt so happy to watch it because a man climbed monkey bars higher than my house, and there was someone else who was stuck in a see-through ball and she opened the ball by doing the splits. We were so happy, it was the best day of the week, but when we were watching the man on the monkey bars, he did flips and tricks. It was the best day ever.

Isla Sutton (9)
St Mary's CE Junior School, Old Basing

Mario's Big Adventure

Today I was finally at Bowser's castle in this multiverse. It was really hard to get to. I was jumping from world to world and pipe to pipe. Sometimes I would be lucky and find a secret pipe that led to a world that was hard to get to, but here I am, to face off the final guardian. I hope I win the battle and if I do, I'll go to an all-new multiverse and I can recruit more Marios (and maybe find the legendary Kirby in a different universe!).

Jesse Agyaba Afriyie (9)
St Mary's CE Junior School, Old Basing

Dear Diary

So on Saturday, I decided to play with my Lego and it took so long to build, but after two long, boring hours, it was complete! So I took it outside, but I dropped it! So I went back inside and into my room and rebuilt it and it took an hour, but I rebuilt it. "Yay!" I screamed. So I took it all again and I didn't drop it. It was good to play with. The next day, I took it home. When I got home, I went to bed and I had a snooze.

Spencer Andrews (9)
St Mary's CE Junior School, Old Basing

We Tried...

Dear Diary,

At the weekend, my brother and I tried some dried fruit. We tried the dried pineapple, and on Saturday, we went swimming. We went swimming at Queen Mary's College and went to get dried fruit at Festival Place. I felt really happy when I tried the dried pineapple pieces because it was the best thing I had ever tasted with fruit. We did some front crawl swimming.

Rose Williams (9)

St Mary's CE Junior School, Old Basing

New Game

Dear Diary,

On Friday, I downloaded Rocket League Season 10. A new update came around. There's lots of new stuff. There are new cars, new boosts, new goals, explosions, and a new stadium.

It made me feel happy. Every season you get a free item in the item shop. This season it's about International Women's Day.

Jack Fox (8)

St Mary's CE Junior School, Old Basing

The Incredible Diary Of A Snowflake

Dear Diary,

I was high in the clouds, falling from the sky. I was a glittery, shiny snowflake, settling on cars and rooftops below. I was feeling happy and excited as I was fluttering to the ground. It made me smile when a young girl was going really fast on her red sledge over me and my snowflake friends.

Sophie Rolls (8)

St Mary's CE Junior School, Old Basing

The Snow Falling From The Sky

Dear Diary,

Today was a super cold day. I was in the clouds with my family. I was white and beautiful, falling from the sky. My family and I landed on the ground together. A little girl came outside and turned me into a snowball. I had so much fun!

Annabelle Huxham (8)

St Mary's CE Junior School, Old Basing

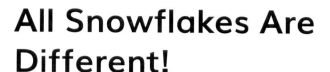

All Snowflakes Are Different!

Dear Diary,

Today I was feeling flabbergasted. I was falling continuously! I'm a tiny molecule. All my friends and family joined together and we made the craziest snowflake ever! I fell into an inventor's house!

Abeer Pandey (8)

St Mary's CE Junior School, Old Basing

Dear Diary

On November 16th, 2022, a theme park, Alton Towers, would have the most breathtaking night there would ever be! Their most famous roller coaster in the UK would be closing for a major refurbishment. Let's go back to 1994 when an unbelievable roller coaster would open, but in the same year, two other rides opened, named Shockwave and The Big One. 1994 became the year of roller coasters soon after! John Wordley was a popular ride designer, so he built a ride that would make the world so impressed. The legendary ride that is Nemesis Reborn.

Archie Hillier (11)
St Wilfrid's Catholic Primary School, Angmering

Dear Diary

Hello, my name is Tony Pigeon, and today was an extremely peculiar day. In the morning, I was minding my own business (in a tree at the park), when I saw a bright blue light speeding around the park's orchard (where my tree is). I immediately recognised the blur. It was the famous Sonic the Hedgehog. Then I decided to do something dumb. I flew in front of the blue light - phew! He stopped in front of me. I brought him to my friends, Pig-Grooti, Ah-Nah and Rick Fred to have a party with Sonic and his friends.

Delta Murphy (10)
St Wilfrid's Catholic Primary School, Angmering

The Horse And The Mysterious Shell!

Dear Diary,

As I woke up, the feeling in my dusty hooves made me want to prance along the beach. As I galloped through the frothy, refreshing waves, I got a tingly excited feeling! As the hot pink, orangey glow of the sun filled the sky with the most heartwarming view, I heard my buddies whinny. They neighed joyfully, "Penelope, Penelope, come and see this bright, intriguing seaweed-covered shell!" I cantered towards them, tossing my head side to side with my glossy, thick, chestnut mane flowing in the morning breeze. My nose touched the shell. I felt magic!

Francesca Ellyatt (7)

Westwood Primary School, Lowestoft

My Day At The Zoo

Last Sunday, I went on an aeroplane to America to visit the zoo. The aeroplane made me feel excited because this was my first time. At the zoo, I saw lots of animals. My favourite animals were the giraffes. They were beautiful, as tall as the clouds, and they had really long eyelashes. One of the giraffes even ate my chocolate chip ice cream. He was a very naughty giraffe. When I was leaving, I began to feel sad.

On my way home, I bumped into Father Christmas. He told me I've been a really, really good girl this year.

Ciara Pettinger (6)

Westwood Primary School, Lowestoft

Kidzania

Dear Diary,

When my best friend and I went to Kidzania, we thought there was going to be a hairdressing job, but no, there wasn't. So we did fashion designing and midwifery, which wasn't delivering babies. It was just taking care of them. We also did cabin crew. For lunch, we had a slush, nuggets and chips. We tried to get on the ambulance after but it took too long. We spent about three and a half hours getting there! It was my first time on the Tube.

Marnie Baldry (7)

Westwood Primary School, Lowestoft

Bad Guy

Dear Diary,

My name is Donna and I am a spy. I catch bad guys and villains. I live in Paris and I help to save the world.

Today, I used my laser beam eyes and saw a bad guy on the run. She had stolen an old lady's purse. I shot her with my laser beam eyes and I gave the purse back to the old lady. She was very happy and said thank you. I felt very happy. This was all in a day's work.

Leni Tuttle (7)

Westwood Primary School, Lowestoft

Hawkleaf School: A New Term

Dear Diary,

It's a new term at Hawkleaf School, I don't think I will make it through this term without getting the cane (yikes!). But at least I have Ariadne, my BFF. We were being driven to Hawkleaf with our suitcases (she'd had a sleepover the night before) and I noticed there were no leaves flying about and it was unusual. We walked through the hall and no one was there. "We might be early," I said, but Ariadne wasn't looking at me. She pointed at the clock. "We're late," she said. We both shuddered. It was the afternoon (*gulp*).

Esme Tory (9)

Youlgrave All Saints CE (VA) Primary School, Youlgrave

The Girls Who Love Horses

Dear Diary,

Today was the best day ever. At school, there's a little girl and her name is Jasmin. She is so kind, but the bad thing is she doesn't have any friends. She walked to the bench, I followed her and as soon as I got to her, I said, "Hello." Well, since it'd been so long and she hadn't said anything, I said, "Do you like horses?"

She looked at me and actually said, "Yeah, they're my favourite animal."

And I said, "Me too!"

So she invited me to her house and we talked about horses a lot.

Daisy Bingham (10)

Youlgrave All Saints CE (VA) Primary School, Youlgrave

Dear Diary

God made the world all in seven days. Day one, he made light. Day two, atmosphere or firmament. Day three, dry ground and plants. Moon, stars and sun on day four, birds and sea creatures on day five. Day six, land animals and humans, and lastly, day seven was the Sabbath of Rest. God is known as the creator or sustainer and the ruler of the universe! There are different names for God, such as Allah, Yahweh, Elohim, Baha'i and Ahura Mazda. Many people don't believe in God, but people who do are Christians. God created the universe and everyone.

Darcy Moorhouse (10)

Youlgrave All Saints CE (VA) Primary School, Youlgrave

Diary Of A Pen

Dear Diary,

As you know, I'm an extremely smart pen and I always get every answer right. Today, and I hate to tell you this, but I got something wrong! My incredibly stupid owner threw me in the bin and got a new pen! Luckily, I got revenge. I waited until he had gotten out of his seat to go to break. I scribbled over his test answers. He got everything wrong and it serves him right. I now have a new owner who is really nice. I am going to try a lot harder for her. Bye for now!

Imogen Room (11)

Youlgrave All Saints CE (VA) Primary School, Youlgrave

Oriel's Diary

Friday 10th March 2022

Dear Diary,

My little brother has come into our world, but I have to share a room with him! I have the best room ever and my mum says I have to share a room and I don't want to. It is a disaster! Well, at least I have someone to play with and I get more toys. Mum says I have to take my brother to school. Well, preschool. I don't want to because I will be late for school. I have to get a haircut today with my brother. I want an undercut, yay!

Oriel Carlin-Monkhouse (10)

Youlgrave All Saints CE (VA) Primary School, Youlgrave

YOUNG WRITERS INFORMATION

We hope you have enjoyed reading this book — and that you will continue to in the coming years.

If you're the parent or family member of an enthusiastic poet or story writer, do visit our website **www.youngwriters.co.uk/subscribe** and sign up to receive news, competitions, writing challenges and tips, activities and much, much more! There's lots to keep budding writers motivated!

If you would like to order further copies of this book, or any of our other titles, then please give us a call or order via your online account.

Young Writers
Remus House
Coltsfoot Drive
Peterborough
PE2 9BF
(01733) 890066
info@youngwriters.co.uk

Join in the conversation!
Tips, news, giveaways and much more!

 YoungWritersUK   YoungWritersCW   youngwriterscw

Scan to watch the
Incredible Diary Video

YoungWriters® — Est. 1991 —